This book is dedicated to Sir David Attenborough
and everyone doing their part to protect our planet.

Chloe the camel

Reece May and
Alexandra Ball

Chloe the camel lives in the Sahara,
With her best friend, a camel called Lara,

Chloe and Lara both have one hump,
Camels are gassy and sometimes they trump!

The Sahara is hot and full of sand,
You won't find much food or water in this barren land,

Chloe and Lara don't need water too much,
But when they drink, it's in a big rush!

Chloe and Lara were out looking for food,
When Lara saw a bush, that put her
in a mood!

"This bush is spikey; we cannot eat it!
I'm done with this desert; I want to quit!"

"Lara, we are camels, our lips are really thick!
Come on let's eat this tasty shrub up, real quick!"

The friends felt a wind that was out of the norm,
"*Oh no!*" said Lara, "*Here comes a sandstorm!*"

Lara was scared and didn't know what to do,
"Come here, Lara. Let me help you"

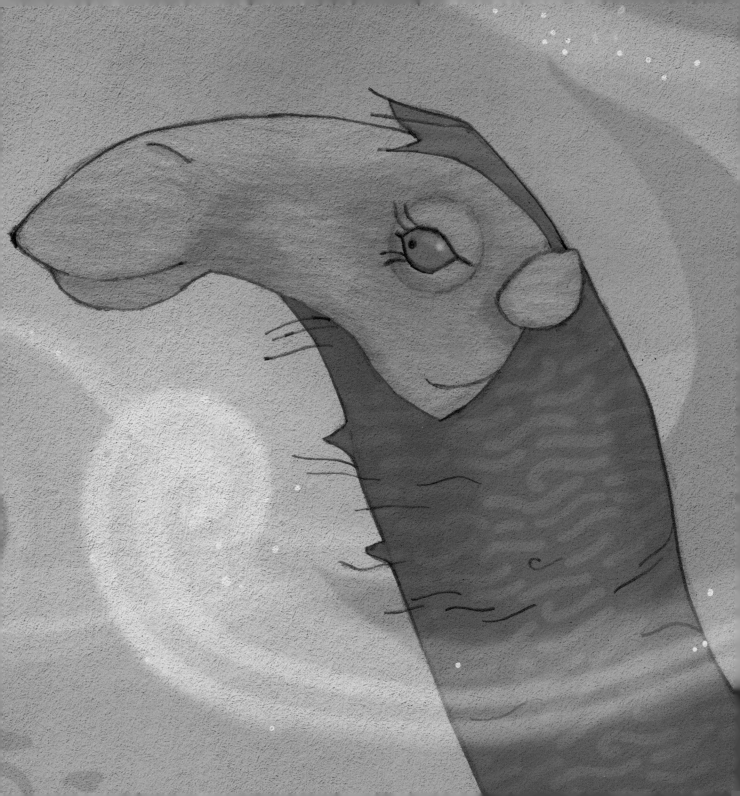

"Sit down on the sand, close next to me,"

"Shut your nostrils and eyes,
We'll be fine you'll see!"

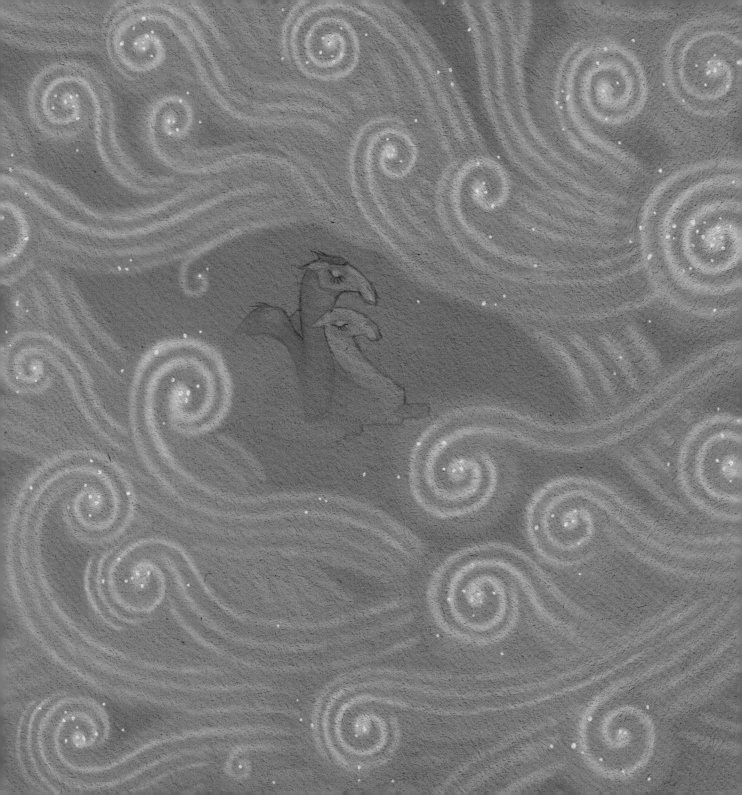

The wind made the sand fly
everywhere,
but Chloe and Lara felt
safe as a pair.

The wind calmed and the sand fell from the sky.
Chloe had a peek, from one of her eyes.

"Lara, I think the storm has gone.
Let's get up and carry on!"

"Chloe, I always feel safer with you."

"That's because we are safer when we travel in a two"

Chloe and Lara remain as best friends,
It's a bond forever, that never ends.

Fun Facts: Camels

There are 2 types of camels!
One humped, **Dromedary** camels, and **two** humped, **Bactrian** camels!

Camels **humps** store fat which
they can live off
for **weeks** or even **months**!

Camels have **three** sets of
eyelids and **two rows of**
eyelashes!

Camels can run
at **40 mph.**

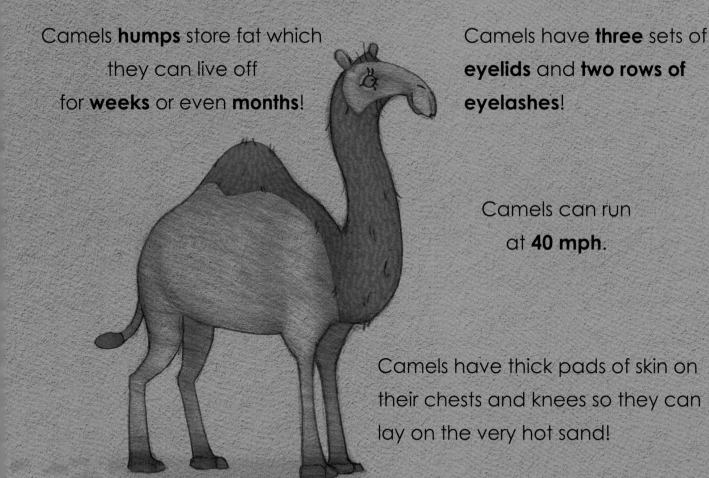

Camels have thick pads of skin on
their chests and knees so they can
lay on the very hot sand!

Angry camels sometimes **spit** as a way to **distract** whatever
they think is a **threat**.

A souvenir guide

Greyfriars House and Gard‹
Worcester

Julie MacLusky

National Trust

A Medieval Survivor

Greyfriars is a remarkable specimen of a timber-framed town house of the 1480s.

Constructed for Thomas Grene in a decade that sits between the late Middle Ages and early Renaissance, Greyfriars only got its name in the late 19th/early 20th century; it refers to a 'friary' though we're not sure what or where this was. Since Grene, it has been the home of well-connected Royalists who helped protect King Charles II in the Civil War; it was the site of butchers, bakers and leather-makers; and, in the 20th century, it became the subject of a long-running battle to save Worcester's heritage (see pages 10–15). It ultimately ended up in the hands of siblings Elsie and Matley Moore, who helped save this remarkable building from destruction and left their distinctive mark in almost every room. Today Greyfriars and its neighbouring buildings on Friar Street provide the opportunity to walk in a street that has not changed much since the late Middle Ages.

Medieval Worcester

Worcester was a garrison town (a place where troops were permanently stationed) during the Wars of the Roses, which dragged on for 30 years. By 1480, as Thomas Grene was making plans for his prestigious house to be built, the Wars were coming to a close.

Left The front of Greyfriars

Top right A detail of the front of Greyfriars and its timbers

In 1485, Henry VII was crowned. The peace that followed meant Worcester had to adapt from being a garrison town to a trading centre. The city prospered because of its position as a market town and service centre for a vast rural hinterland.

An unusual requirement

At the time Greyfriars was built, and continuing into the 16th century, all men were required by law to practise archery every Sunday; this was held at The Butts on a site now close to Worcester's bus station.

Crafting Greyfriars

In an age when successful men had limited ways to display their wealth, a timber-framed house such as Greyfriars could be used by men like Thomas Grene – who was elected High Bailiff (a legal position of law and order) in 1493 and '97 – to let the city know he had 'arrived'.

The master craftsmen of the 1480s who designed and built Greyfriars lived in an era when a war horse was the most prestigious form of transport. Consequently, construction materials had to be found locally, from natural sources. The houses these craftsmen built were well insulated, cool in summer and heat-retaining in winter, with easy maintenance.

It's in the details

The external triangular shape of the two large gables with a long level roof between is typical of the grander merchant houses of the 15th century. In Greyfriars, timbers are arranged in a pattern with lots of diagonal pieces to act as braces. The strong wooden frame is then filled in with all sorts of other materials, which can include brick, 'wattle and daub' or rubble.

From the street the vivid, black wooden skeleton of close-studded oak that enabled the building to survive for over five hundred years can clearly be seen. Wood is one of the oldest and most versatile building materials: incredibly strong and easy to carve. Its only drawback is a vulnerability to rot, so late medieval owners would protect it using the same lime wash used to coat the panels between the timbers.

Opposite In this image, you can see Greyfriars' triangular gables and the long level roof between

Above left The gateway arch as seen from the back of Greyfriars. The shield with the three Catherine wheels is that of the Street family who once lived here (see page 7). The others are those of notable Worcester families

Above right Details of Greyfriars' timbers, in which you can see carpenters' marks

The timbered frame ends in two short wings that flank the courtyard. The wealth and power of Thomas Grene is shown through the lavish use of expensive timber and its decoration. Slender columns topped by moulded caps, bases and brackets are carved into the exposed timbers facing the street. On the gables above there are richly carved bargeboards – few of these have survived on similar buildings. This decoration is better preserved in the arches of the gateway entrance, where Thomas Grene's initials are carved into the jetty brackets framing the entrance.

A practical design

Greyfriars has a 'jettied' upper half, so the upper floor projects beyond the floor below. This was a useful feature when chamber pots were emptied from the upper stories into the streets.

Not everything landed in the street, however – in the 16th century, records show that one of the building's residents, a Mrs Goodlack, paid eight pence to have a 'gowte' in the city wall – this was probably a hole to throw rubbish through into the town ditch, which ran along the bottom of the garden.

War and disease

The Battle of Worcester.

Thomas Grene only got to enjoy the house he had built for about fifteen years – he died in 1499.

In 1501, Richard and Pernell Grene inherited their father's 'tenement and brewhouse'. By 1523, Greyfriars had been sold to Thomas Twesyll.

Twesyll was acquainted with Thomas Cromwell, Chief Minister to King Henry VIII. In 1532, when Twesyll fell upon hard times, he appealed to Cromwell for support. Twesyll was granted £10 a year (the equivalent of almost £200,000 today), because of his 'services to the Queen consort Jane Seymour'.

The Streets

After Twesyll died in 1544, Greyfriars saw a succession of owners and tenants until 1566, when the house was bought by Francis Street the Elder. Francis's descendants lived in Greyfriars for almost a hundred years. Between c.1600 and 1610 one of these, Francis Street the Younger, sold the house to the city council for £100, then rented it on a 400-year lease for £5 per year. He used the money from the sale to install the new staircase up to the Gallery and contemporary windows, and extended the north wing. Today this extension provides an example of the shift from the close timber frames to more open, brick-filled panels.

In August 1575, 10 years after Francis Street the Elder moved to Greyfriars, Queen Elizabeth I visited Worcester. A month before, the city council met to arrange the cleaning and decoration of the city; Friar Street, for once, would have been free of accumulated livestock and human waste. During her visit, the Queen met prominent citizens. At the time, Francis was working his way up the city's hierarchy – he became High Bailiff in 1568 – and it's likely he would have been among those introduced to her.

The Streets in the Civil War

Worcester was one of the cities most affected by the violence of the Civil War. It was the first to declare its support for King Charles I and the last to surrender.

George Street, a staunch Royalist, became Mayor of Worcester in 1635, but lost his place on the council when the Roundheads (Parliamentarians) were gaining power in 1642.

George died in 1643 and his wife died from the plague the following year. Greyfriars was passed to their sons, John and Thomas, who would have been living in Greyfriars when King Charles II sought refuge in the city just before the Battle of Worcester in August 1651.

R. White delin. 1684.

THOMAS STREET MILES }
Justiciarius Comunis Banci . ~ } Ætatis 63.

Pub.d Feb.y 20.th 1794 by W. Richardson, Castle St. Leicester Square.

Within a few days of Charles' arrival, the city was fortified 'beyond imagination'. Nearby Friars Gate was made secure. Sleeping in the house must have been difficult, knowing that the city was depending upon the medieval wall at the bottom of Greyfriars' garden to hold Oliver Cromwell's New Model Army at bay.

Despite these precautions, the Royalists lost the battle – although Charles managed to escape. Special aid was granted to churchwardens to bury the slain Scottish soldiers and provide perfume to mask the smell of the corpses. Greyfriars would not have been a pleasant place to live.

The defeat meant Cromwell's rule was secure, and within nine years the Royalist Street family had left Greyfriars for good. However, Thomas Street prospered during the Restoration of the Monarchy in 1660; he became MP for Worcester five times and was knighted in 1681.

Opposite *The Battle of Worcester, 1651*, an engraving by Barlow made in c.1750

Above A line engraving of Sir Thomas Street, published by William Richardson; after Robert White. It was originally published on 20 February 1794

A place
of business

Daniel George took advantage of Worcester's population increase by building ten houses in his back garden; construction work took place during 1828–32. Known as George's Yard, this was one of many courts built behind the homes of wealthy residents at this time – the city's population tripled to 46,000 during the 19th century, and the development of housing was a useful source of income. (Find out more about George's Yard and its residents on pages 16–19.)

Greyfriars' new look

The Georges went bankrupt in 1850, at which point they sub-let the section south of the gateway to Henry Schaeffer, a clothes salesman and Jewish refugee from Germany. (Schaeffer may have later converted to Anglicanism – his children were all baptised at Worcester's Angel Street Congregational Church.) Schaeffer prospered; by 1861 he'd moved out and had shop windows and doorways added to the front of Greyfriars, creating opportunities for a range of retail businesses. He eventually took over the entire property in 1871, keeping one of the shops for his own gentlemen's outfitters business. Schaeffer owned Greyfriars until 1883, when he sold the lease to Thomas Allen, a clothier.

After the Streets left in 1660, Greyfriars once again became home to a number of short-term residents until 1699.

This was when local baker Richard Maris moved in and began dividing the house. In 1724 Greyfriars' north wing was sublet to the George family, who were also originally bakers. They stayed for more than ninety years, taking over the whole house when Maris died in the late 1740s.

Which shops were here?

Over the years, Greyfriars' shopkeepers included a greengrocer, an umbrella maker, a bookbinder, leather maker, milliner, tinsmith, dealer in second-hand books, and even a fish fryer.

In 1838, Daniel George set up a 'kiddlywink', Old Oak Tavern, in Greyfriars' north front. 'Kiddlywinks' were beer houses licensed to sell beer or cider by Customs & Excise rather than the traditional magistrate's licence. They were also reputed to be the haunt of smugglers.

The tavern's scrubbed floor was sprinkled with sawdust, and customers would have drunk quarts of fresh, unaged beer, known as 'mild', by the light of paraffin lamps and candles.

George ran the pub until 1849, when it was taken over by Joseph and Harriet Ingles. It eventually closed in 1879, perhaps due to tough competition: during the years it was open, the number of taverns grew to such an extent that there was one pub for every 178 people.

Greyfriars also housed a bakery; its remains can be seen in the Hall (see pages 22–23), around the fireplace. This was probably a side-flue oven with a brick-built arch and a flat, tiled floor.

Layout

In the 1830s, Greyfriars' shops were the width of a typical house, operated from the front room. The retail area was small with a limited supply of goods on display – the majority of the stock was kept behind the counter and out the back.

The last shops

By 1912, Greyfriars' roof was described as sagging and dilapidated, allowing rain to soak the rooms below. The roof was repaired and the shops stayed open until 1922, when a client took over the whole space and opened it as 'The Olde Curiosity Shoppe'. But by the 1930s, the house was mostly derelict: only the north wing was occupied, by the Canadian Stores grocery – and this was gone by c.1936.

Left Friar Street in 1906

Above An illustration of Friar Street as it was in 1850, when Schaeffer owned Greyfriars

Above right The Canadian Stores grocery, the last surviving shop in Greyfriars

Saving Greyfriars

The fact that this home has endured for over five hundred years is remarkable in a city once infamous for the destruction of its heritage.

In the 20th century, derelict Greyfriars attracted the attention of the Worcestershire Archaeological Society, the authority on local historical buildings. They discussed a possible tenancy of the building with the current owner, Reverend Allen, a retired vicar in Bournemouth who had inherited the property.

Negotiations dragged on until 1934, when Reverend Allen was ordered to submit proposals to repair the building; costs were estimated at £170. This was a time when the average annual wage was £100 and Reverend Allen baulked at the cost. In 1936, Mr Allen pulled out of the scheme and the city council issued a demolition order.

This is where Greyfriars' story might have ended: it had outlasted plagues, the reigns of 22 British Kings and Queens, the Reformation, the Civil War, the Industrial Revolution and the First World War, but its fate rested on the ability of a retired vicar to come up with £170 for repairs.

Fighting for Greyfriars' survival

Exhausted by years of negotiations, the demolition order galvanised the Archaeological Society's members. The Society's President, a Mr Knowles, told members that Greyfriars was one of Worcester's most beautiful houses, of exceptional historic interest, and could, if it were judiciously handled, become a moneymaking asset for Worcester. Members discussed using Greyfriars to celebrate the lives and history of people in Worcestershire. Pressure was put on the council through local media.

Despite the Society's best efforts, negotiations with the council dragged on. At one point Reverend Allen, fed up with negotiations, said he would like the building pulled down. But the Archaeological Society did not give up.

Greyfriars' first saviour: Major Thompson

On the outbreak of war in 1939, all demolitions were ordered to be postponed until the end of hostilities. This provided the Society with more time to find the money to save Greyfriars.

In 1943, a member of the Society's committee and a former High Sheriff of Worcestershire (he held the role in 1941), Major William John Thompson, offered to buy Greyfriars' lease from Reverend Allen and the freehold from the city council for £1,000; the equivalent of about £42,000 today, the price was considered very low – but by this time the city was only too glad to get rid of responsibility for the building.

After purchase, Major Thompson spent another £1,500 of his own money to carry out emergency repairs, investing the equivalent of £105,000 in the property overall. He maintained Greyfriars until 1946, but could not afford to cover the running costs indefinitely. The Archaeological Society did not have sufficient funds to take it on either. Once again, Greyfriars' future was at risk.

Left A portrait of Major WJ Thompson (artist and date unknown)

Far left Major Thompson's heraldic shield, which can be seen above the fireplace in the Hall

Restoration and restoring

When Major Thompson couldn't afford to continue restoring Greyfriars, siblings John Malcom Matley Moore and Florence Elsie Moore (commonly known as Matley Moore and Elsie Moore), along with their mother, Florence, offered to restore the building at their own expense providing they could use it as their home during their lifetime.

They also insisted that the tenants of George's Yard (see pages 16–19), which was still occupied by ten families, must be prevented from using the front gate to the building.

Major Thompson donated the property to a charitable trust set up by the Archaeological Society; he maintained an interest in Greyfriars, staying on as President of the Trust until his death in 1959.

After negotiating the change in the right of way, Major Thompson had a solid wall built across the arch at the back of Greyfriars to completely block the George's Yard tenants' access. From then on the Yard's families had to use a new entrance that was installed down a narrow passage at the side of Greyfriars and emerged into the Yard by the first terraced house. This route was closed when the houses were demolished in 1955.

'The work of preserving this house has been immense: it could not have been done at a worse time for materials and labour and of necessity it has been costly: but if it had been delayed any longer, the building would have been past all care. A thing of beauty from the past has been saved to give pleasure to those of the present and, it is hoped, future generations who care for these things.'

Matley Moore

Above right and above far right
The back of Greyfriars before (left) and after (right) restoration work

Right and far right The north wing of the house before (left) and after (right) restoration work was completed

Restoring Greyfriars

In 1949, when Greyfriars was physically separated from the residents of George's Yard, the Moores moved into the house.

Much of what you can see at Greyfriars today was brought here by the Moores. Members of the Archaeological Society, who had been part of the long struggle to save Greyfriars, were happy to help the siblings out; in a time of post-war scarcity, many were downsizing and gladly passed on the furnishings for which they no longer had room.

The Moores exploited other social connections to find out where bargains were to be found. In the aftermath of the Second World War, many homeowners faced financial hardship and the Moores would be given tip-offs about pieces that were appearing at auction houses and sales throughout the Midlands. Many years before the expression was coined, the Moores were expert 'upcyclers'. However Greyfriars was not allowed to become overcrowded with furniture; if something new was acquired, something else had to go. One such item was a suit of armour, known as Eustace; when it was sold at Sotheby's, Matley took it to London by train.

Stories were told of army lorries pulling up with 'found' materials that were swiftly unloaded in the back yard. Timber was taken from derelict barns, sometimes without the owner's knowledge. Labour was scarce and Matley used contacts in the army to have German prisoners of war quietly brought in to help; one soldier from Bavaria proved very useful, as he had experience of the restoration of timber-framed buildings.

The National Trust inherits Greyfriars

Matley died in 1982 and Elsie in 1985. In 1966 Matley had arranged for the Archaeological Society to donate Greyfriars, along with other properties on Friar Street which were saved by his sister (see pages 14–15), to the National Trust. In their wills, the Moores left the entire contents of the house to the Trust with the wish that the house should have no barriers or ropes, allowing visitors to roam freely.

The Moores at Greyfriars

Both Matley and Elsie were prominent figures in the Worcestershire Archaeological Society and many of Greyfriars' visitors and volunteers have shared their memories of the family with us.

A simple life

The siblings were born in Wilmslow, Cheshire, to a dental surgeon – who died when Elsie was only three – and his much-younger second wife, Florence. The family made their money from owning a substantial amount of property.

Elsie and Matley lived frugally and kept Greyfriars badly lit and cold. However, they were generous to many people, supporting their window cleaner when his wife died and helping poor boys with their education.

The pair did enjoy the occasional luxury; they visited Italy and every year went to Somerset for three weeks, always staying in the same hotel. They travelled separately and took their own cutlery and crockery.

A hair-raising ride

A drive with the Moores was not for the faint-hearted. They ignored other traffic and insisted on staying in top gear for hundreds of miles. Elsie always took her own vehicle, an elderly, draughty Bedford Dormobile campervan with lots of blankets.

A woman of art

Elsie had an unhappy childhood; it appears her mother preferred male children and didn't have a lot of love left for her daughter. But in adulthood, Elsie became a respected authority on medieval artwork and gave talks about her work at the Commandery in Worcester. She also took part in the restoration of King John's tomb in Worcester Cathedral and her designs were used as altar cloths.

Elsie was outspoken with a sense of humour, and her frustrated artistic talents found expression in her work on Greyfriars. Always working in dungarees, she painted much of the walls and furniture in the house in her distinctive shades of red, green and gold, which still feature heavily here. Nothing went to waste: clothes were made with bits and pieces from the house, including a grey coat with fringing made from rug tassels.

After her mother's death in 1953, Elsie relished her financial independence (until that point, it appears Florence controlled the family's money). In 1960–3, she used her own money to save the three shops opposite Greyfriars from demolition. This wasn't a totally selfless decision, however – by owning these shops, Elsie could ensure her view from Greyfriars wasn't ever altered.

Elsie never married. When a visitor held Elsie's hand in hospital and kissed her, Elsie, who was then aged 82, said 'That's the first time I have ever been kissed'.

A man of science

Matley was described as abrasive and diabolical in a crowd. He liked to complain, but feared his grumbles being published, so – with the exception of some *Country Life* articles – he wrote them all in a private journal. On his death this was sent to the county records office, not to be opened for 50 years.

Despite all this, Matley was said to be a kind and learned man, charming in limited company, with an immense knowledge of art, architecture and local history.

Matley followed his father and grandfather into the medical profession, becoming a dental surgeon and serving in the Royal Army Medical Corps in 1917, during the First World War. He later worked in Worcester, running both private and public practices after the NHS was introduced; he saw his private patients in a surgery he set up in Greyfriars' north wing, in the former greengrocer.

From 1923 to 1969, Matley was Excursion Secretary for the Worcestershire Archaeological Society and was a mine of information on which houses were worth visiting and their owners. His summer programmes were enviable and his excursions are legendary, especially the strict discipline he imposed with the aid of his whistle. Whistles can still be seen around the house, such was Matley's fondness for using them to bring people, including visitors at Greyfriars, to order.

Above left Originally published in the *Worcester Evening News* in 1970, this is the only photo we have of Elsie and Matley Moore together as adults. A copy is on display in the Library (see page 31)

Below left The gates showing the Moores' heraldic shield were donated to Greyfriars by the Moores' mother, Florence. Each gate contains one of her initials

Above right Elsie's sewing box, which can still be seen at Greyfriars

George's Yard

Built from 1828–1832, George's Yard was home to around fifty people for most of its existence.

Its three-storey terraced houses, each with their own small garden, offered conveniently located, cheap housing at a time when affordable, well-designed homes were only available to those living close to factories run by visionaries like Cadbury in Birmingham. As such, demand for the properties here was strong – George's Yard's residents came from all over Britain, and the houses were continuously occupied from 1830 to 1955.

But although the Worcestershire Archaeological Society saved Greyfriars, they didn't look to purchase George's Yard, so the council issued a demolition order. In 1955, the remaining residents were rehoused and George's Yard was knocked down to make way for Greyfriars' garden (traces of it can still be found there, see pages 34–36).

Above George's Yard after demolition

Above right The barn, toilets and wash house at the end of the Yard

Below right A Victory over Japan (VJ) Day party in George's Yard, August 1945

Life in the Yard

The architecture of George's Yard created a unique, and mostly now lost, way of living. Life here provided stability: young women married into the families of men who had grown up in the same row of houses; families lived close to parents who could support them by providing childcare; help was given to those who were struggling financially. Years before the creation of the welfare state, the working poor who lived in this housing constructed their own support networks.

Football and television

Many of the children of George's Yard's last residents remember it positively. They felt better off than others, with cleaner clothes for school. One family even had a television and took summer holidays. They could also safely play together outdoors: games of football, tennis and cricket sometimes meant balls went over the wall into Greyfriars, but the Moores used to throw them back. One resident later said he liked the way there were 'always plenty of kids mucking about'.

Making a living

Working conditions for 19th-century residents of the Yard were harsh. The 1878 Factory and Workshop Act eventually banned children under 10 from working, and limited women's work to 56 hours a week. However, pressure was still put on children to find work at an early age, or to assist their relatives, as was the case for two former residents of George's Yard: John Snape helped with the family pig business on Sundays, while, from the age of 13, Jeff Bullock delivered newspapers for a shop in neighbouring Pump Street.

Before 1891 parents had to pay for their children's education, so many never went to school. After 1891, school was free for children under 11, but was designed to produce obedience and 'habits of cleanliness', rather than provide access to better paid work.

Jobs held by the residents of George's Yard included: driver, painter and decorator, greengrocer, removal man, cleaner, soldier, storekeeper, factory worker, café assistant and shop assistant. Such work was highly valued: the last residents described how they felt well off, because everyone worked. They described people on Tolladine Road, Worcester as poorer because they went hop and potato harvesting.

Some women worked out of their homes in George's Yard, washing the laundry of middle-class families, and sewing, tailoring and glove-making.

Not an easy life

Many of the comforts we take for granted today – clean streets, flushing toilets, regular waste collection – would have seemed luxurious to George's Yard's residents.

Dirt, disease and sewers

Like all 19th-century towns, Worcester was filthy and unsanitary. Outbreaks of cholera in 1832 and 1849 killed 128 people. However, in the later 19th century the water supply was improved. George's Yard's residents used a well for water but in later years a standpipe was installed – they were still using this in the 1950s.

In the early 1930s, tenants depended on coke or coal for heating, and coal was still used in the 1950s.

Toilet talk

We're not sure exactly when residents here began to enjoy flush toilets, but we do know the council was installing mains water and sewerage in the late 19th century. Until then, residents' waste was collected inside the toilet blocks in a bucket and the excrement covered with soil to reduce odour. While the city slept, the night soil cart toured the streets, removing the contents of the buckets.

A load of rubbish

For George's Yard's first 100 years, there was no regular refuse collection in Worcester. The last residents of the Yard describe how, even during the mid-20th century, a 'pig bin' was set up in the yard, where they put vegetable peelings that were carried to feed pigs kept on the west bank of the river Severn, a way of working introduced nationally after the Second World War. In winter the largest sow would be killed and meat would be given to each household. This made a welcome change from the rabbits that provided the most affordable meat.

The wash-houses

George's Yard had two sets of toilets and wash-houses, used for washing clothes and bathing. One was at the top of the Yard and one was at the bottom. Families were told which one of these to use. They could use the wash-houses once a week, and were allocated a morning or afternoon for doing so.

For many years, the residents built up a bonfire for Guy Fawkes in front of the wash houses at the top of the Yard. The children collected fuel from local shops and then sold it to the rag & bone man for money for fireworks. But sadly one year the Guy was vandalised when it was started up before 5 November – from then on the families went elsewhere to enjoy a Guy Fawkes bonfire.

Find out more
Historian Anna Frankel has uncovered a wealth of information about the lost history of George's Yard, with the help of contributions from the children of the last people to live there in the 1950s. This recent research is accessible and held by the National Trust.

Above left Washing strung out across George's Yard

Below left The houses of George's Yard

Below right Families of George's Yard

Exploring Greyfriars

Today there are six rooms and a garden to explore at Greyfriars, left as the Moores lived in them. Each gives an insight into the siblings and the many families who preceded them.

The Entrance
The entrance to Greyfriars from the street is through a big double gateway. This provided much-needed security for the building's residents before the creation of a professional police force in the early 19th century. In addition to the gates, night watchmen and guard dogs could have been stationed here to keep the building's owners safe from harm.

The carpentry
The initials 'TG' carved into the jetty brackets framing the entrance from the street are those of Thomas Grene, who had the house built. The woodwork here is elaborately carved and ornamented. It is high enough to save those arriving on horseback from having to dismount before they were safely out of the street.

Right The rear of Greyfriars, as seen from the garden

Some of the original 15th-century carpenters' marks can be seen high up on the timbers in the archway. Oak-timbered buildings have frames that are created from quite short, thick timber pieces. The wood is prepared off-site and marked by the master craftsmen to help with assembly. Similar markings are still used by local craftsmen working on the construction of modern timber-framed homes.

The passage

A cobbled passage under the archway leads into a small courtyard, where the second set of gates is decorated with the coat of arms of the Moore family and their mother Florence. The rest of the porch is the original work of the 15th-century craftsmen.

Top The passage leading to the garden and entrance

Left The front of Greyfriars, as seen from the street

The Hall

For most of the building's existence, this Hall was two separate rooms. It was only knocked through into one _c._1916 by Thomas Frost, who wanted to create a large display space for goods in his second-hand furniture shop.

When the Moores lived here, the Hall was used as a meeting place for the Worcestershire Archaeological Society. The frugal siblings kept Greyfriars badly heated, and winter meetings were bitterly cold – Elsie and Matley would turn on a two-bar electric fire, but it barely penetrated the chill.

The panelling
The panelling on the south wall probably dates from between 1580 and 1630, when the Street family lived here (see page 7). The rest was put in by the Moores and came from a variety of sources. The section under the windows was probably from a 17th-century Sidbury house scheduled for demolition; another came from a funeral parlour that made way for Worcester's King Street car park. The panelling on the staircase wall was rescued by Homery Folkes, an architect and close friend of the Moores, who found it being used as fencing on a building site and covered in paint.

Makers' marks
You can see the original 15th-century carpenters' mortise slots and dowel holes in the central ceiling beam. These are used by carpenters to join pieces of wood that connect at 90 degrees, without the need for nails. Some of the tenon joints, used to hold the old wall, can also still be seen in the ceiling beam.

The oak prop was installed to support the first floor once the dividing wall was removed.

The tapestries
The wood panelling is decorated with two tapestries which dominate the room.

Above the high table is a Mortlake tapestry, woven in the late 17th century. Many of the Mortlake tapestries depicted classical mythology; this one tells the story of Alpheus and Arethusa from the Metamorphoses of Ovid. In the original, Arethusa is described as bathing naked, however here the designer has chosen to show her bathing in her hunting outfit.

The tapestry at the other end of the room is from Brussels, woven in the 16th century. Powerful state and religious rulers used flamboyant tapestries like this to signal their wealth and power. It shows St Paul pleading at his trial before Agrippa, and depicts an evangelist in each corner.

Top A view of the Hall, including the fireplace and Mortlake tapestry

Left A framed piece of flock wallpaper

Right One of the doorstops Elsie salvaged and painted. These now sit the in fireplaces around the house

The oak chest
Sat below the Brussels tapestry, this chest is possibly 15th-century and one of the oldest pieces at Greyfriars.

Around the fireplace
The fireplace would have heated the second room. The overmantel embroidery was worked by Elsie Moore in 1970; it shows flowers of all seasons and contains an extract from a Thomas Arnold poem *Lines in a Kensington Garden*. The heraldic shields below are those of Major Thompson (see page 11) and the Moores (the Moores designed their coat of arms themselves, having not inherited one).

Salvaged objects
Many of the items in this room are examples of objects rescued by the Moores.

The collection of painted iron doorstops in the hearth came from Padmore's, a major Worcester foundry (metal castings factory). When Elsie heard of its closure in 1967, she headed over to the foundry with a wheelbarrow, returning with a collection of cast-iron doorstops. She then painted them, mostly in her favourite colours: red, green and gold.

The Georgian stone floor was brought from Wychbold Hall near Droitwich, which was collapsing because of brine extraction, (a different way of producing salt).

The long oak table, dating c.1630, came from the estate of Marie Corelli, a celebrated Victorian author read by Queen Victoria, William Gladstone and Winston Churchill. Matley Moore acquired the table at a three-day auction of Corelli's possessions in 1943, following the death of her companion Bertha Vyver. Matley would have had to work his way through crowds of fans that fought to get some small memento of the author.

The Staircase,
The Side Gallery

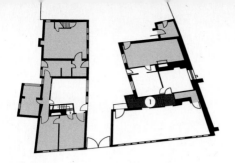

1. The Staircase

The original staircase is claustrophobic, very narrow and blocked off – another narrow staircase was later installed at the other end of Greyfriars, in the Library, so residents could go upstairs at either end of the house, but not in the middle.

The Streets, a large family, installed a wider staircase sometime between 1603–1610, during their alterations to Greyfriars; this joined the two ends together. The present staircase is a restored version of this.

The tapestry that hangs over the top of the staircase is 18th-century from Brussels and was given to the house by Major Thompson.

Famous doors

Backing onto the staircase are two elaborately painted, 16th-century cupboard doors which are covered in Tudor badges, arabesques and coats of arms.

The doors were originally made by Reeves of Bewdley in about 1540. The panels that have been used in the doors were from a house scheduled for demolition. They were rescued by James Lees-Milne, former secretary of the National Trust's Country Houses Committee, but, as he didn't have space for them, gave them to Greyfriars. Elsie was well-known to Lees-Milne owing to her expertise in medieval decoration.

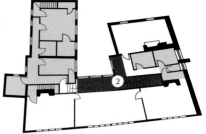

Matley Moore made the six-panel screen, placed on the stair wall, from recycled 17th-century Dutch painted leather.

The gallery windows are not original but were replaced in the 1940s and show 30 painted birds. They were designed by Mr Kaines-Smith, a keeper of Birmingham Art Gallery and an acquaintance of the Moores.

The large curtains at the side, which open onto the Parlour, were copied from the museum of St Mark's Cathedral, Venice. Elsie stenciled the pattern and then painted the fabric.

Left A detail of one of the painted birds from the gallery windows

Below right A sampler by Mary Moore, dated 1788

Far left The staircase installed by Francis Street the Younger in the 17th century

2. The Side Gallery

In contrast to the lower floor, the furniture and wall coverings throughout the upstairs rooms come from a wide range of periods.

To the right at the top of the stairs is a red and gold Italian silk appliqué wall hanging, estimated to be early 18th-century; its receipt indicates it was an 'early altar frontal'.

The china on display is part of a large collection of oriental pieces – smaller items are displayed in the alcove at the end of the Gallery. Close to the alcove are five samplers (embroidery pieces, produced to demonstrate the needlework skills of the artist). Two show the name of Moore and are dated from 1830, and one, from 1788, shows the name of a great grandmother. Another has the name of the maternal grandmother, Matley. It was begun by 8-year-old Georgina Barret in 1851, but finished by the same Georgina when she was 83, in 1926; by then her name had changed to Georgina Matley, as she had married into the family.

The Parlour

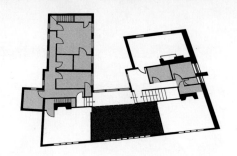

This was the Moores' sitting room, where they kept up with the news by reading *The Times* every day. They had no television as Matley hated having anything that made noise in the house (Elsie had an old radio, held together with rubber bands, but had to keep it in her bedroom). When Matley died in 1982, Elsie bought herself a transistor radio.

Fireplace and features

When the Moores moved in, there was no fireplace here, yet such a feature was essential for a sitting room. So they installed an overmantel – a bed headboard that came from The Tything, their former family home, and which had been in their family for 200 years. It is dated 1616 and inlaid with the initials IR (for King James I), and carved with bog oak and holly. Below the mantel, William Morris-style tiles surround the fireplace.

To the left of the fireplace there is an English, *chinoiserie* style painted screen, dating from 1695. It was bought in 1947 for £10 from Brockhampton House in Herefordshire, while the Moores were waiting to move into Greyfriars, and was later repaired by Elsie.

The ceiling beams in this room are original but Francis Street the Younger added the panelling with its carved frieze in the early 17th century. The frieze features the Streets' shield, bearing three Catherine wheels sitting among Welsh dragons.

The furniture

The striking standard lamps were recycled from bedposts, then painted by Elsie.

The chestnut table is 17th-century Spanish and was given to Greyfriars by Captain Berkeley as a thank you to the Moores for helping with the opening of Berkeley Castle, Gloucestershire. The court cupboard is late 16th-century. The longcase clock was made in Worcester by Sam Cocks and has just one hand; hours, rather than minutes, were more important when it was made in the late 1600s.

The tapestry is late-period Mortlake or Soho and tells the story, from Ovid, of Arcas and Callisto, and how they were turned into the Great Bear and the Little Bear in the night sky.

Opposite The Parlour, set up as if waiting for Matley and Elsie to come here and read *The Times*

Left *A Small Boy standing at the Gate of a Ruined Cottage* by Benjamin Williams Leader, 1858

The Moores' sewing features in this room: Elsie embroidered the crewelwork cushion in the high back chair and her sewing bag hangs near the fireplace. The other armchair shows Matley's needlework and is based upon the flock wallpaper in the Hall. The leather-covered box was made by Matley Moore using leather left over from the folding screen in the Hall.

On the right of the fireplace, the 1858 oil painting is by the Worcester artist Benjamin Leader, whose family home is now Worcester's Diglis House Hotel, overlooking the River Severn.

The Bedroom

This was where Matley Moore slept; Elsie's bedroom was in the north wing and is now used by a tenant of the National Trust.

There were no springs in Matley Moore's 16th-century, four-foot double bed, which is hung with early 20th-century Liberty fabric. The bed instead has a rope hold; at night Matley would have had to pull the ropes tight himself.

Designs and details

This room has no panelling, so the original framework of the house can be seen more clearly; the stone fireplace is also original.

Crewelwork and the wall hangings

The wall hangings are 17th- or early 18th-century crewelwork. Crewelwork dates back as far as the Bayeux Tapestry – the pattern (here it is of the tree of life) is embroidered in wool onto linen. This fabric was given to the Moores with its top edge damaged, so Elsie had it altered.

Furnishings

The cradle dates from 1729 and was owned by the Moore family. Cradles could be narrower than today because babies were traditionally swaddled tightly to prevent movement.

The spice cupboard is early 18th-century.

The large painting is *Fête in a Tivoli Villa* by Henry Andrews, in the style of the early 18th-century French painter, Watteau. Opposite the picture is a rare, *c.*early 16th-century hanging cupboard, believed to be the second-oldest piece in Greyfriars.

Above A view of the Bedroom

Left *Fête in a Tivoli Villa* by Henry Andrews I, fl.1830–d.1868

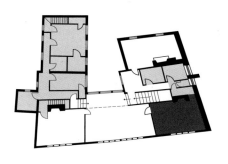

Below left Some of the doorstops salvaged and decorated by Elsie

Below far left A close-up detail of the bedroom's crewelwork wall hangings

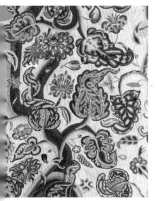

The dowry chest

Dating from 1806, the Dutch dowry chest originally belonged to Maria Heisman, whose family moved from Bavaria via Holland to settle in Cheshire, close to the Moores' home town. It is very heavy but has handles on each end and a big lock, presumably for ease of transport during migration.

A *trousseau* was a way for a young woman to save up for marriage and contribute to her new home. At the time this chest was made, and up until the 1870 Married Women's Property Act, a woman's possessions became her husband's after marriage. Women had no right to property; the law did not recognise them as separate from their husbands.

The collection of a trousseau was a coming of age rite for young women even up to the 1950s; it was also referred to as the 'bottom drawer', 'hope chest' or 'glory box' and would hold clothing, table linen, towels, bed linen, quilts and sometimes tableware.

The Library

The Moores' books sit on opposite sides of the room: the fictional are Elsie's, and the non-fiction and historical books, and albums of *Country Life* are Matley's.

The collection is typical of a late 19th- and early 20th-century middle-class family. Matley concentrated upon antiques, architecture, country life, histories and travel books. Meanwhile Elsie's shelves have novels, poetry and the psychology texts that she took up with later in life.

Between the bookshelves, there is a pencil sketch of Matley from 1917, when he was serving with the Royal Army Medical Corps.

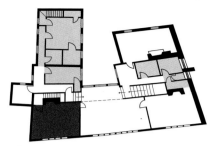

The table
This room contains a copy of the only adult photograph of the camera-shy Moores. Sitting on the table, it was taken by a newspaper photographer in 1970, when Matley received a Civil Trust Award for the restoration of Greyfriars.

The table itself is thought to be 1930s, from South Africa; the lamps are *c*.late 16th-century Spanish candlesticks, recycled by Elsie. Also on this table is some of Elsie's calligraphy.

Paintings and tapestries
The English watercolour on the side of the window shows Friar Street in 1859, and is by the 19th-century painter Thomas Shotter Boys.

The 16th-century Flemish verdure tapestry shows Abraham and Isaac; the chair in front is by William Morris, 1906. William Glover made the clock in Worcester around 1770.

Opposite top Matley's bookplate showing the Moores' heraldic shield. The shield was designed by the siblings – they did not inherit one

Opposite bottom A view of the Library

Among the boxes covered with leather left over from the screen in the hall, there are two from the 17th century, from Plas Newydd in North Wales (also National Trust).

In the watercolour by Ursula MacDonald (to the right of the window, as seen from the doorway), a dilapidated Greyfriars can be seen before its restoration. The standpipe that provided water for George's Yard is clearly visible.

A piece of history
The brass plaque above the bookcase is another example of how the Moores helped salvage Worcester's history and heritage: it was saved from the tomb of George Street and his wife when St Andrew's Church was demolished in 1949. Today only the spire from the church remains, as 'The Glover's Needle' next to the River Severn.

Above left A black and white version of Ursula McDonald's watercolour, dated 1946. It depicts a dilapidated, pre-restoration Greyfriars

The Dining Room

Originally used as a kitchen, this room is part of the original 1480s building; the Moores later redecorated it to fit with an 18th-century dining suite.

The wallpaper

Bright, extremely rare, almost 300-year-old Georgian wallpaper panels dominate this room; the pattern was originally hand-blocked on, then overlaid with silver foil to simulate satin and the back stamped with a George I excise duty mark.

Rolls of this paper were rescued, unused, from the attic of a rectory at Birlingham near Pershore. Elsie used the paper to decorate panels, but when she heard arsenic had been used in the green colour, and that Napoleon was supposed to have died from arsenic poisoning, she pinned brown paper over the panels to protect herself – holes made by pins used to hold the paper in place can still be seen.

The furniture and decorations

The wall decoration fits with the original Georgian dining table. The chairs are late 18th-century Hepplewhite style by Gillows of Lancaster, a prestigious furniture maker.

The feature alcove housing a display of china, to the side of the fireplace, was built into an existing plain domed recess. This provides another example of the Moores' 'recycling' efforts – the alcove was rescued from a house that was demolished during the redevelopment of Worcester in the 1960s.

The recess houses a Spode, Copeland and Garret green and gold bedside wash set; this consists of a jug, bowl and other pots for powders and so forth, and was used for washing before bed and in the morning. There are also some Japanese-style yellow vases. (There isn't a single piece of Worcester china in the house; for some reason the Moores did not collect it.)

The miniature ovals include images of Elsie aged about three, her father and maternal grandparents, and an unknown gentleman in a winged collar.

The 18th-century mule chest got its name from being 'neither horse nor donkey' – it is a mixture of a chest of drawers and a lift-up chest. The style was popular from 1600–1700 in England and colonial America.

The 18th-century mahogany clock was made by Thomas Adams of Middlewich, Cheshire, and has a moon that comes out at night.

Below left A close-up view of the Georgian wallpaper

Bottom left A view of the maiolica tiles over the fireplace, and Spode, Copeland and Garret ware

Below A partial view of the Dining Room, including a feature alcove

Maiolica

'Maiolica' describes tin-glazed pottery created during the Italian Renaissance. It employs strong colours on a white background and shows mainly mythological and historical scenes. It was produced across smaller cities in central and northern Italy for the luxury European market.

The tiles over the fireplace are an example of 16th-century Italian maiolica, and are 'painted with stories', or *istoriato*. Brought to the house by Florence Moore, they show the anointment of David, the presentation of the Ten Commandments, and baby Moses.

The Garden

It is hard to imagine that this was a rubble-filled yard when the Moores started work on it.

A medieval status symbol

Originally – in the late medieval era – Greyfriars' garden would have been used to reinforce the high status of the house. Gardens in towns took their inspiration from the formal gardens of the rich, which were designed to provide a retreat from the world and laid out in rectangular plots with herbs and scented flowers. Behind a wattle fence livestock might be kept, such as chickens and a pig – the pig serving as an efficient household waste disposal unit.

Creating today's garden

Work began on the garden after George's Yard was demolished in 1955; it is created to Elsie's design and was made by Matley. The Moores regularly travelled to Italy and the result is an English garden with strong Italianate features. Elsie chose the shrubs and trees, and these are now well established.

Perhaps unsurprisingly, the siblings recycled many of the materials from George's Yard in their new garden. Roof tiles became steps, bricks the patio and rubble was used to create the raised side terrace. A fireplace was even used to create a fountain. The bricks and tiles were also used in the summer house and gazebo. In the gazebo, the marble seat, with its marble back, was once the tops of Victorian washstands in George's Yard – the floor has black and white tiles in the corner, and Gentlemen's Relish pots have been reused as flooring.

A few remnants of George's Yard, including one window, can be seen sticking out of Greyfriars' north wall – they were left to help its stability.

A few decorations

The two dolphins on the semi-circular steps were given by Bertram Clough Williams-Ellis, then owner of Portmeirion pottery, and the terracotta pots on the side terrace are from Hindlip Hall, Worcestershire. There is an Italian oil pot on the round border.

In the summer house, Elsie's painted cloth helps create a surprisingly peaceful retreat in a busy city centre.

Above left Looking towards the side wall of the garden

Above right Flower pots around the rear of the house

Far left One of the dolphins given to the Moores by Bertram Clough Williams-Ellis

Left The garden steps, made from roof tiles from George's Yard

Surrounded by history

The garden is bordered on the east end by the remains of the city wall; from the other side it is possible to see parts of the original Roman wall which dates from AD100. The wall, last reinforced during the Civil War (see page 7), provided Worcester with essential security. Some rocks in the rockery were 'relocated' from the wall.

When the house was built it was close to one of the gates in the city wall, where tax would be paid on goods brought into the city. However, if you were close enough, and it was night time, you could avoid paying taxes by passing goods through the wall; one former resident of George's Yard said she knew the location of such a gap in the wall here.

On the south side of Greyfriars, the brick wall was strengthened in 1836 when the city gaol was built, perhaps because the house's residents were concerned about prisoners digging their way through. The gaol was replaced by almshouses in 1912, but the prison chapel remained and can still be seen from the garden.

Right A view from the garden towards Greyfriars house, including the steps made from the George's Yard roof tiles